CONTENTS

OH MY GOD, THEY KILLED KENNY!

BOY, WHAT THE FUDGE YOU DOIN'?

Pedigree

Published 2011. Pedigree Books Ltd, Beech Hill House, Walnut Gardens, Exeter, Devon EX4 4DH
books@pedigreegroup.co.uk | www.pedigreebooks.com

KYLE BROFLOVSKI

DAMMIT! WHAT THE HELL IS WRONG WITH EVERYBODY?

KYLE IS THE SMART ONE OF THE GROUP, BUT EVERYONE MAKES FUN OF HIM BECAUSE HE IS JEWISH. HE ALSO HAS AN OVERBEARING MOTHER AND AN ADOPTED BROTHER FROM CANADA NAMED IKE.

STAN MARSH

HEY, DON'T BE A BUTT HOLE!

STAN IS THE OFFICIAL LEADER OF THE GROUP AND THE USUAL VOICE OF REASON. HE HAS AN OLDER SISTER NAMED SHELLY WHO OFTEN BEATS HIM UP AND HE OWNS A GAY DOG NAMED SPARKY.

9

ERIC CARTMAN

OH MAN, YOU GUYS SUCK!

CARTMAN IS THE SON OF A SINGLE MOTHER WHO SPOILS HIM TERRIBLY WITH HIGH-FAT TREATS. THE OTHER KIDS TEASE HIM MERCILESSLY ABOUT HIS WEIGHT, AND HE RESPONDS BY BEING INCREDIBLY OBNOXIOUS AND OPINIONATED.

KENNY McCORMICK

OH MY GOD, THEY KILLED KENNY!

WITH HIS ORANGE PARKA DRAWN TIGHTLY AROUND HIS FACE, KENNY'S WISECRACKS ARE COMPLETELY UNINTELLIGIBLE TO THE VIEWER, BUT PERFECTLY CLEAR TO THE OTHER RESIDENTS OF SOUTH PARK.

BUTTERS

It's "THE BUTTERS SHOW"

I NEED TO BEHAVE MYSELF!

WHERE I GO, DISTRUCTION WILL FOLLOW!

SOUTH PARK

COMICS

PROFESSOR CHAOS

CLASHH!

HE PULLS A PIECE OF CLOTHING FROM THE CLOSET.

PREPARE, O LITTLE TOWN!

AND BEGINS TO FEVERISHLY SEW A CAPE TOGETHER.

PREPARE FOR THE GREATEST SUPERVILLAIN YOU'VE EVER SEEN!

PROFESSOR CHAOS

WHERE I GO, DESTRUCTION WILL FOLLOW!

KNOCK KNOCK

BUTTERS, TIME FOR BED.

HU-UH, OKAY MOM.

YES. I SLEEP, SLEEP FOR NOW. TOMORROW, THE CHAOS BEGINS.

SO TODAY WE WENT TO THE AMUSEMENT PARK WITH ALL OUR POSSIBLE FRIENDS.

IT WAS A REALLY FUN TIME. WE RODE ALL THE RIDES AND EVERYONE GOT ALONG GREAT.

I THINK THE PERSON THAT STOOD OUT MOST AT THE AMUSEMENT PARK WAS JIMMY.

THE HAUNTED MANOR

WELL, THE, THE REASON I THINK I WOULD MAKE THE PERFECT FOREH- FRIEND, IS THAT I LOVE TELLING JOKES. YOU KNOW, WHO DOESN'T LIKE TO LAUGH?

TWEEK. NOW THERE'S AN INTERESTING CHOICE. TWEEK HAS A LOT OF QUALITIES THAT I LOOK FOR IN A FRIEND.

27

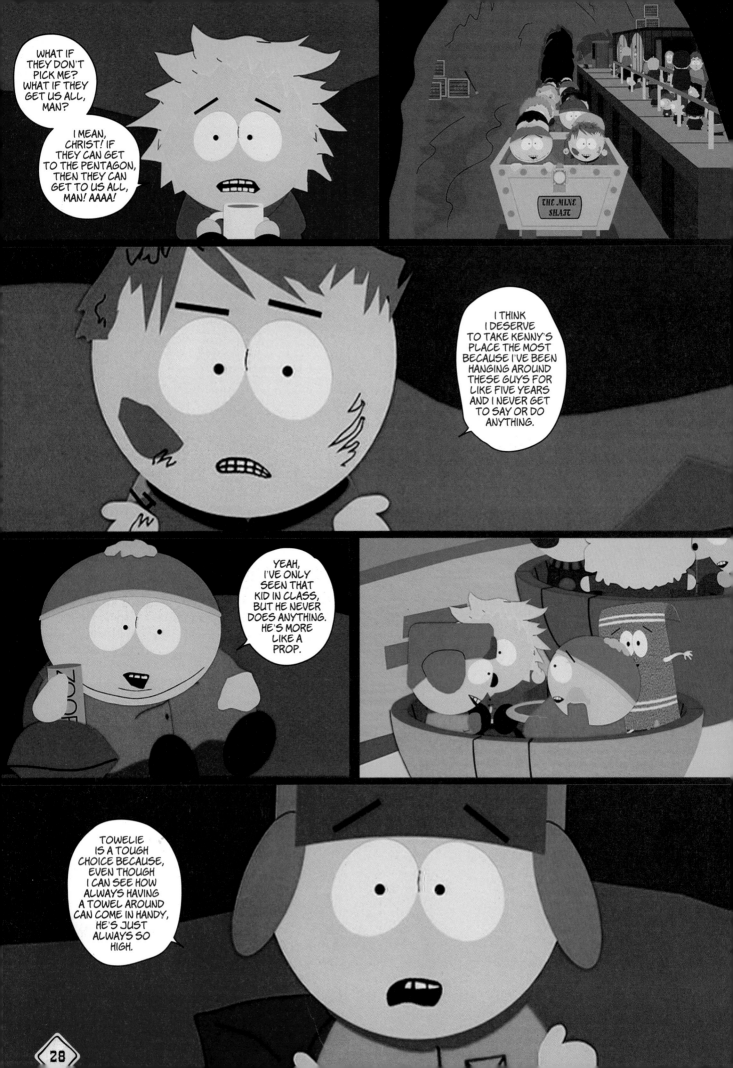

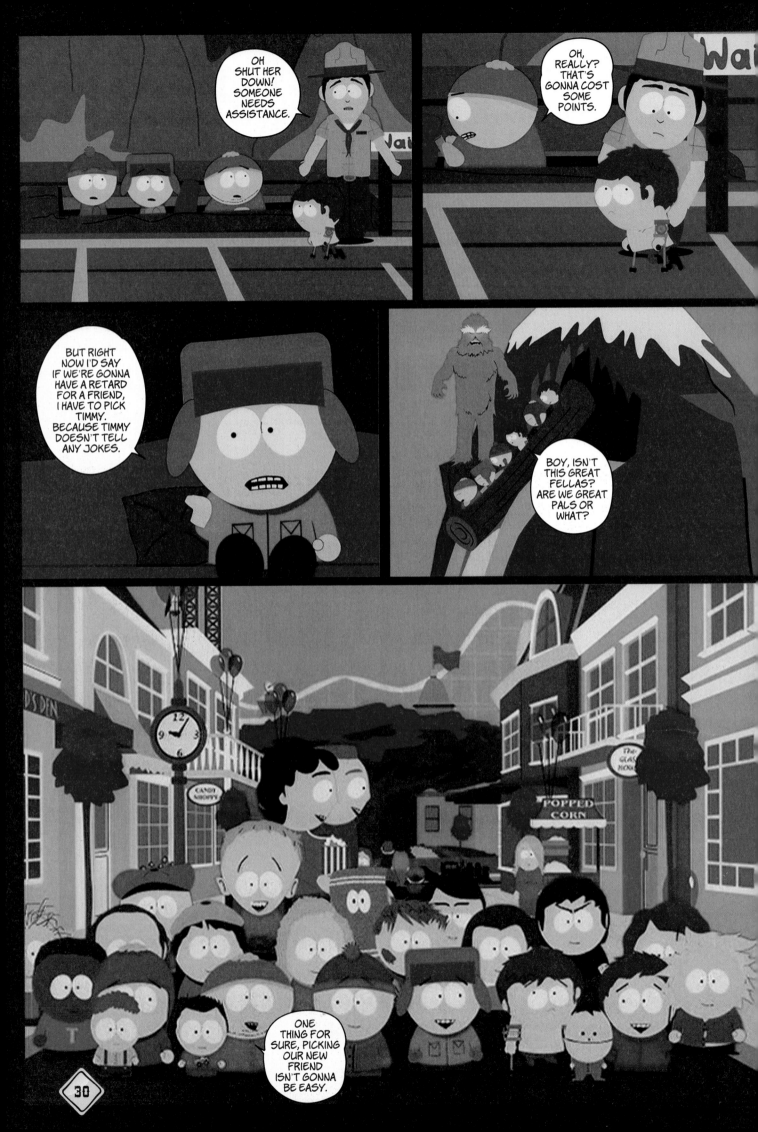

SOUTH PARK TIMES

New Theater To Open In South Park

Job is a jew called the ugh ta park one day to find himself
happening upon a small rock. look, small rock he said, i shall
throw that at that person next to me because he is staring at me
the wrong way. As angel appeared at his shoulder, No jabber jaw,
do not throw that rock, you will become an evil jabber jaw, then
noone will like you and they will call ye a meanie. said, i shall
throw that at that person next to me because he is at

at the ugh ta park one day to find himself
happening upon a small rock. look, small rock he said, i shall
throw that at all people and at his shoulder. No jabber jaw,
do not throw that rock, you will become an evil jabber jaw, then
noone will like you and they will call you a meanie. said, i shall
throw that at that person next to me because he is at

Weather Still Decent

fri	sat	sun

SOUTH PARK MARATHON
A MONTH AWAY

NOW, WHENEVER WE MULTIPLY A NUMBER TIMES FIVE, THE RESULT IS GOING TO END IN A ZERO OR A FIVE.

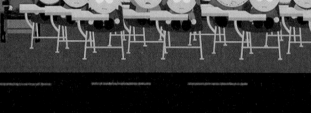

MS. CHOK-SONDIK.

WHAT IS IT, BUTTERS?

AH, ? I NEED TO GO TO THE BATHROOM. REALLY BAD.

OH ALRIGHT BUTTERS. TAKE THE BATHROOM PASS AND GO.

BUTTERS GETS OFF HIS SEAT AND HEADS FOR THE DOOR.

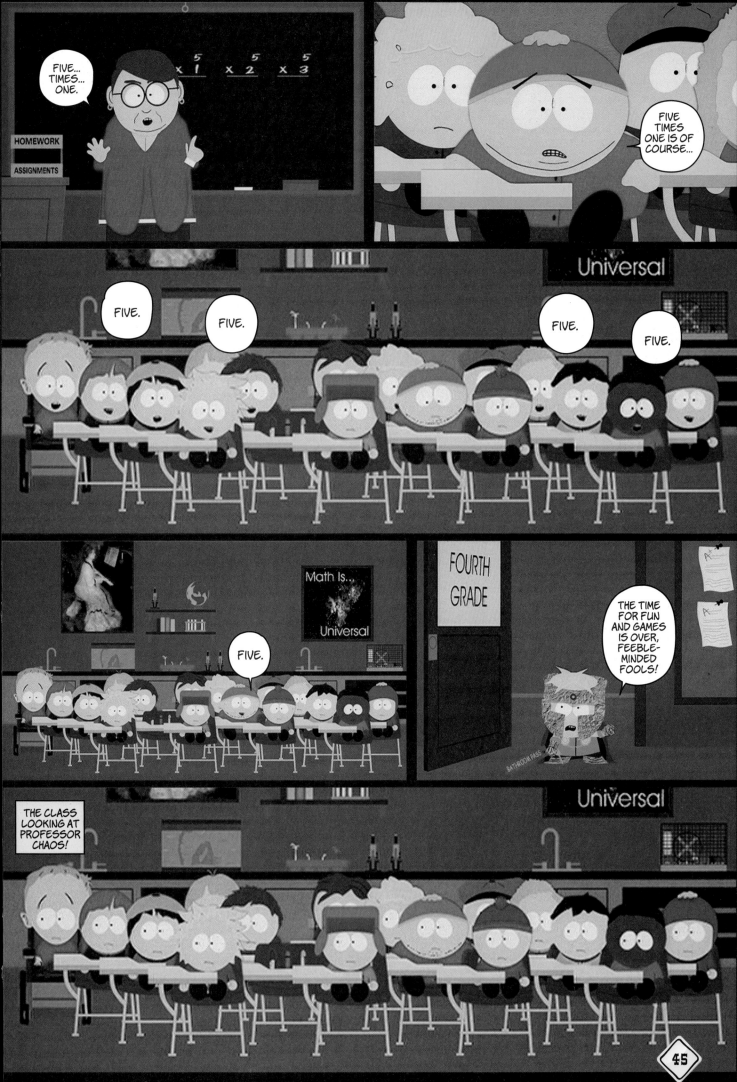

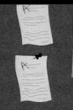

HEY! THAT KID TOOK MY LAST ERASER! COME BACK HERE, KID!

HOMEWORK ASSIGNMENTS

OH! AH, I'M BACK FROM THE BATHROOM. AH I REALLY LET ONE GO IN THERE.

BUTTERS, DID YOU SEE ANOTHER LITTLE KID RUN OUT OF HERE?

WHY YES, I DID. BUT HE PUSHED ME DOWN AND I SCRAPED MY ELBOW.

GO ON AND LOOK AT IT. IT'S SCRAPED. LOOK.

YES. GO ON AND SEE THE RED MARK ON MY ELBOW, THE RED MARK I MADE MYSELF TO THROW YOU OFF PROFESSOR CHAOS'S TRAIL.

FOURTH GRADE

IT LOOKS FINE, BUTTERS. OKAY, HOLD ON AND STAY HERE, CHILDREN.

FOURTH GRADE

HEHE-HEHE...

THE SWIMSUIT COMPETITION REALLY GAVE US A FRESH LOOK AT SOME OF THE CANDIDATES.

WELL, I DON'T THINK I DID TOO WELL IN THE BATHING SUIT COMPETITION.

BUT I CAN'T WAIT FOR THE TALENT SHOW COMPETITION. THAT'LL REALLY BE MY CHANCE TO SHINE.

MR. GARRISON

LIFE ISN'T FAIR, KIDDO, GET USED TO IT.

CHEF

BOY, WHAT THE FUDGE YOU DOIN?

TIMMY

LIVIN' A LIE!

TIMMY!

JIMMY

WOW, WHAT A GREAT AUDIENCE.

JIMBO & NED

SOUTH PARK
COMICS

VOLCANO

YOU WHAT?!?

MOH YEAH, THAT'S RIGHT, I DON'T THINK EIGHT-YEAR-OLD KIDS DRINK BEER, MMM.

I LIKE CHO-COLATE MILK.

BEER

WELL, WE'LL BE DOING PLENTY OF DRINKING ON THIS TRIP.

AFTER ALL, HUNTING SOBER IS LIKE... FISHING... SOBER.

BEER

IT SURE WILL BE NICE TO GET OUT OF THE CITY FOR A WHILE, AWAY FROM CIVILIZATION.

TOM'S RHINOPLASTY

THE TRUCK DRIVES OUT OF THE TOWN AND UP A LITTLE MOUNTAIN ROAD, WHERE IT COMES TO A STOP. THE TRIP IS RIDICULOUSLY SHORT.

VRMMM

WELL, HERE WE ARE.

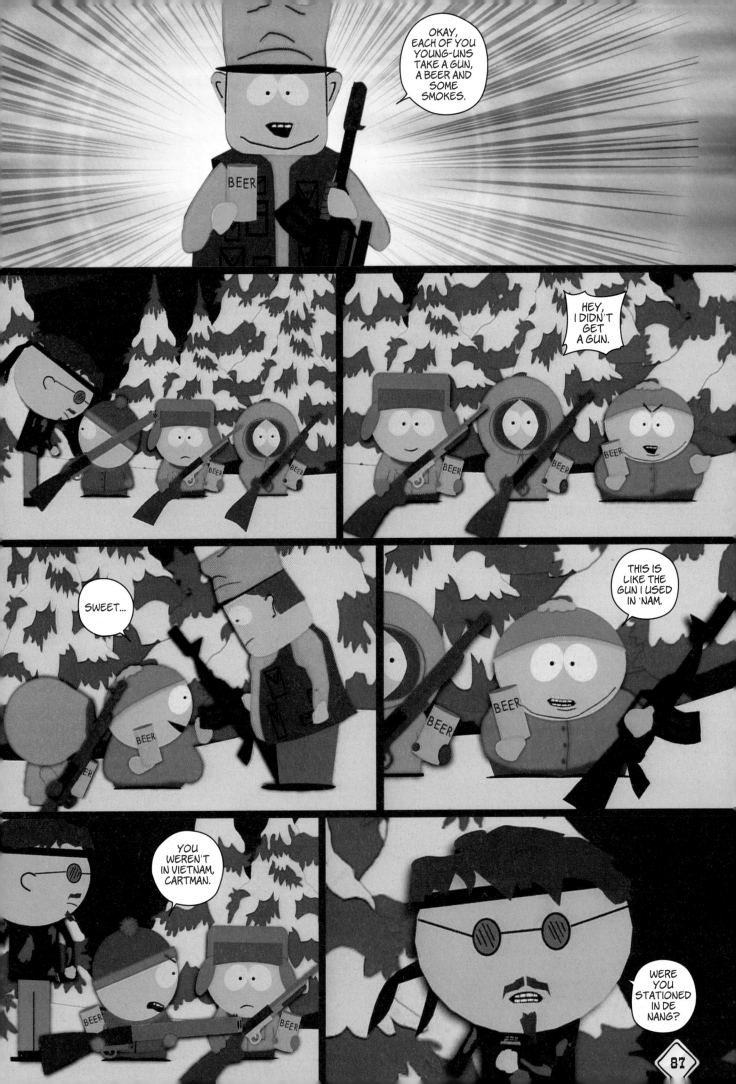

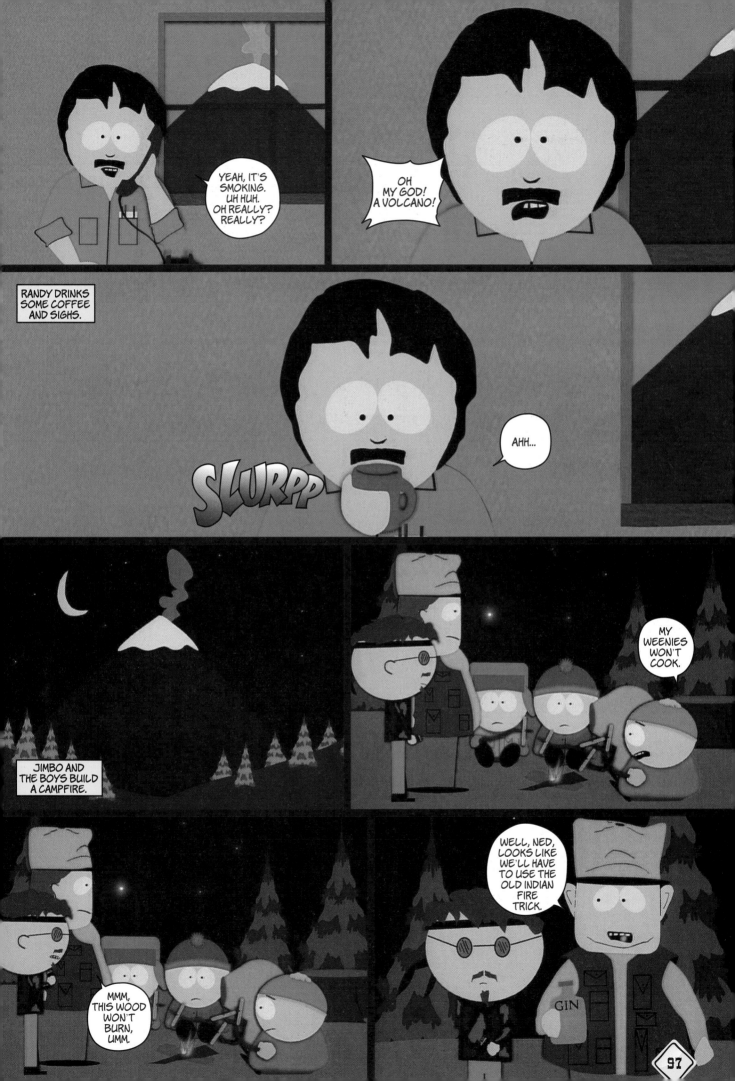

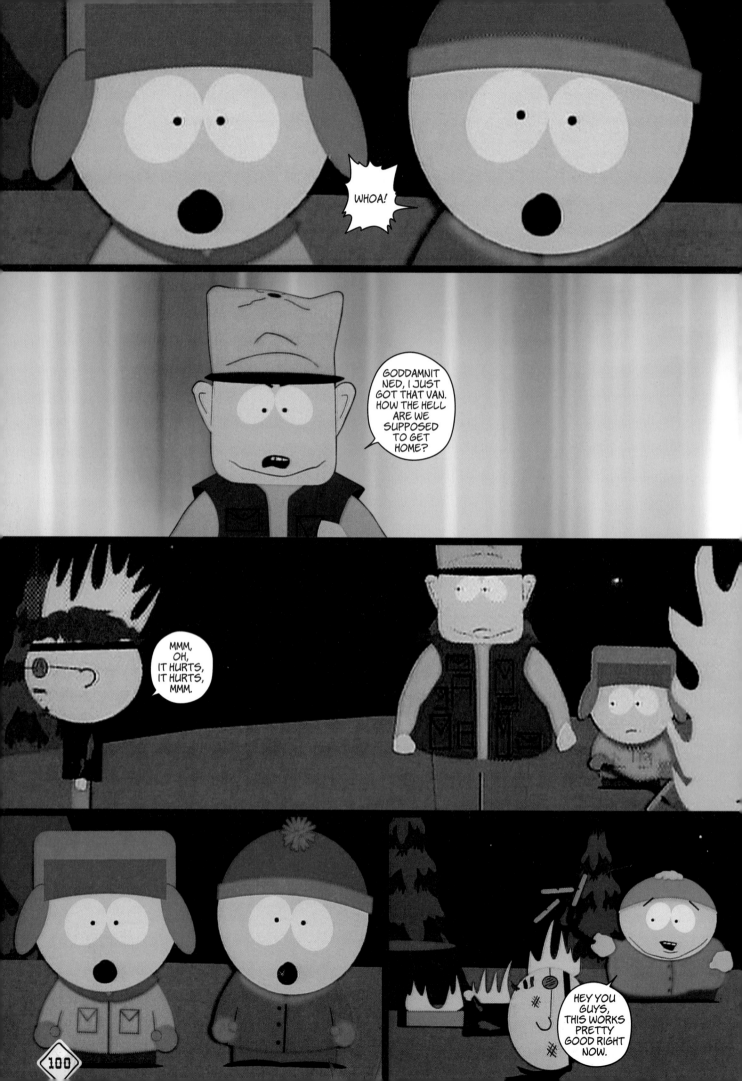

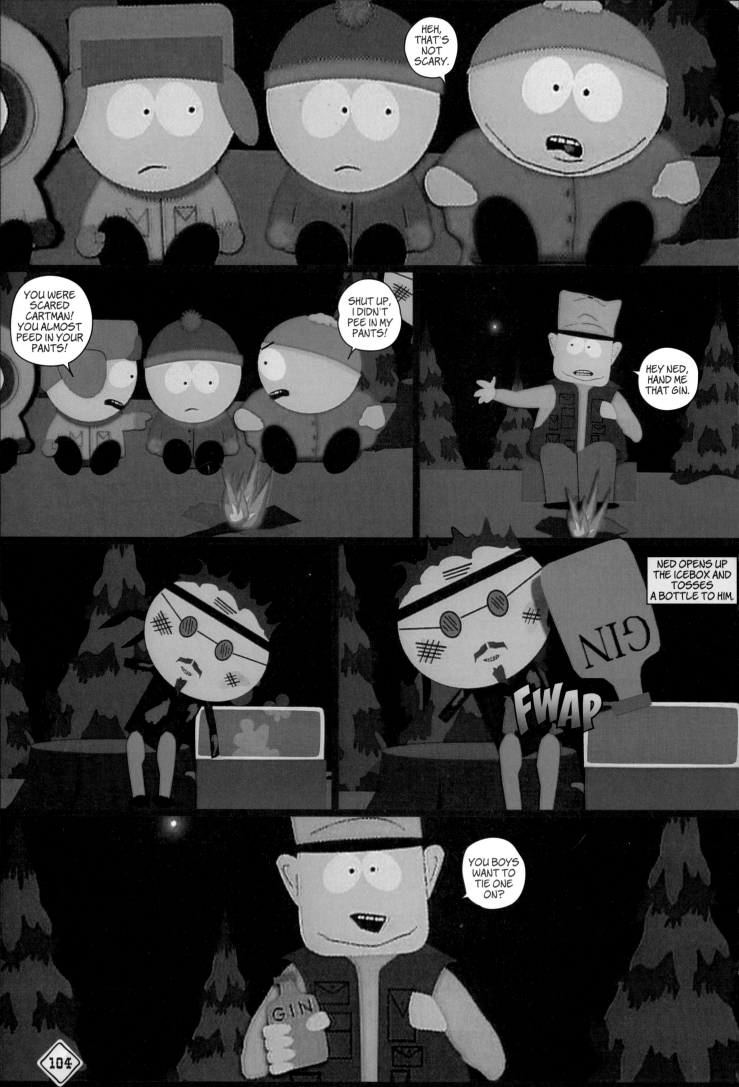

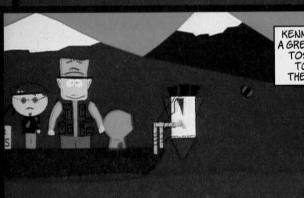

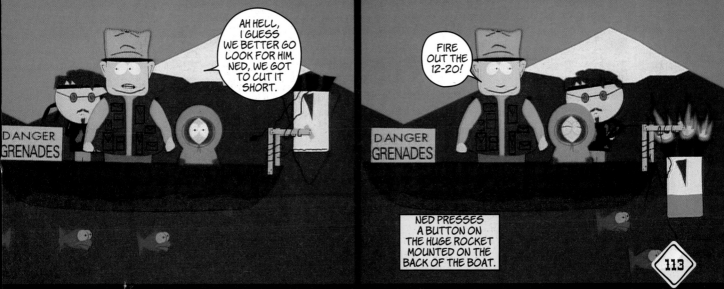

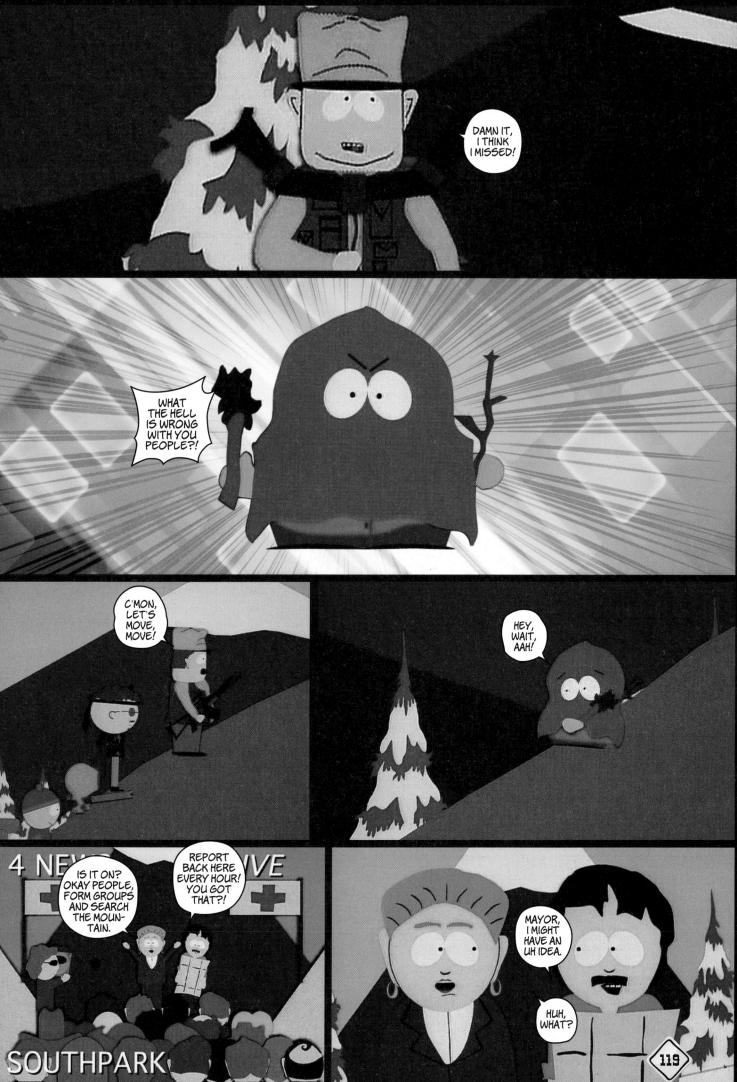

OKAY, ANY QUESTIONS?

1952 copyright

THAT HAS GOT TO BE THE MOST RIDICULOUS LOAD OF PIG CRAP I HAVE EVER SEEN!

THAT'S ENOUGH OUT OF YOU!

1952 copyright

THE GROUP CONTINUES THEIR HOT PURSUIT.

I'M GONNA BAG SCUZZLE-BUTT. THEN WE'LL SEE WHO'S THE LITTLE BASTARD.

HEY, SERIOUSLY YOU GUYS!

KILL IT, STANLEY. KILL IT!

AH, DAMN IT, I CAN'T DO IT!

YOU PANSY! GIVE ME THAT GUN.

CARTMAN MANAGES TO GET OFF HIS DISGUISE.

HEY!

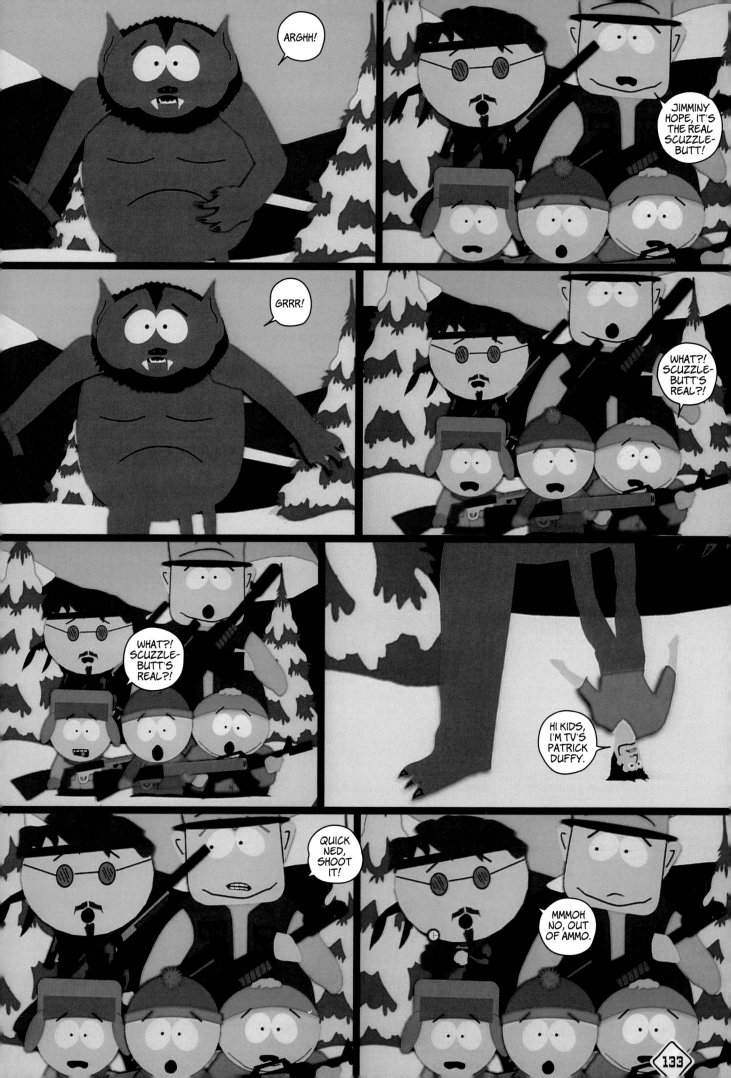

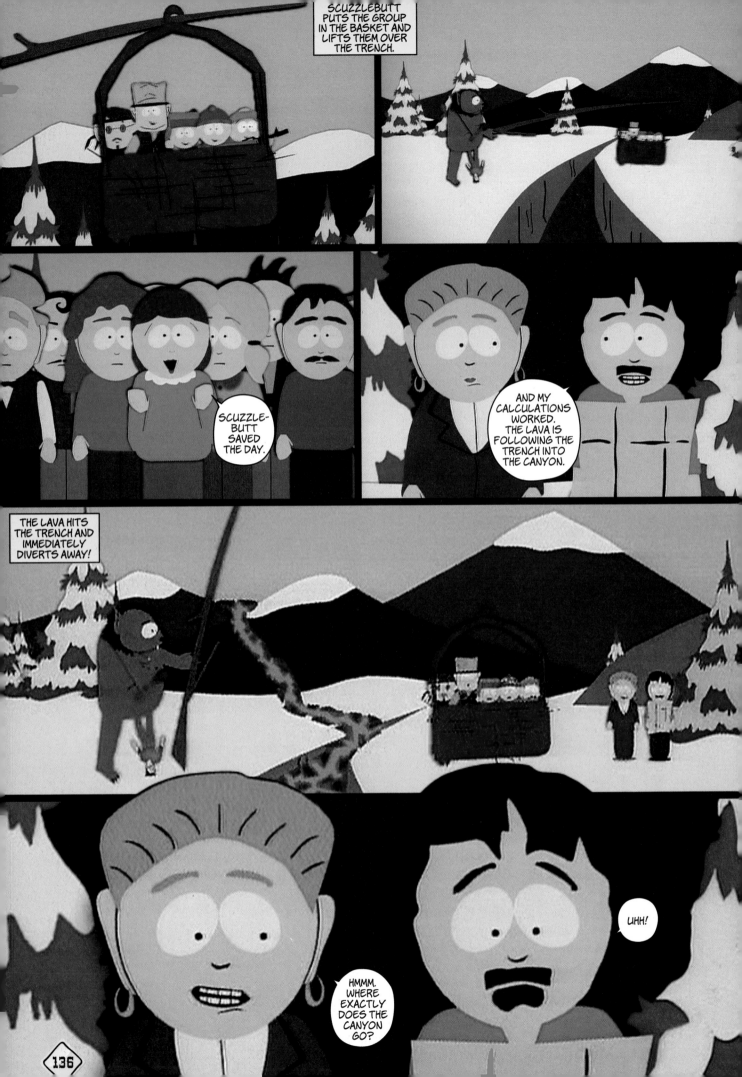

139

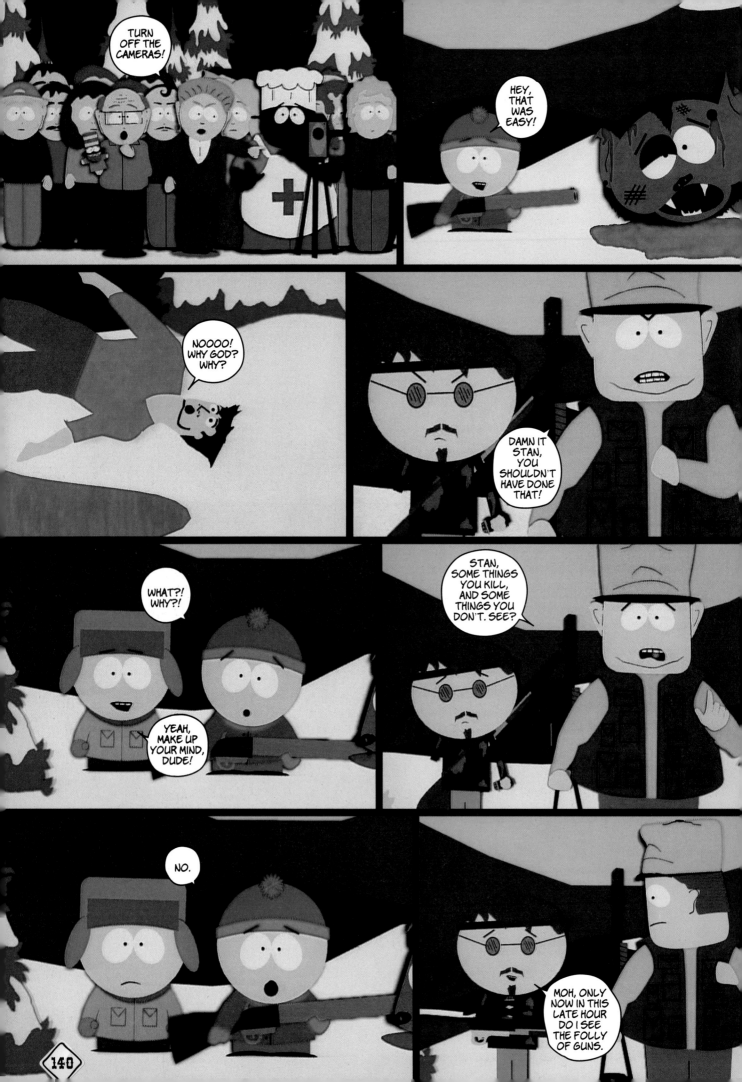